Me And My Alien Friend

Cosmic Poems about Friendship

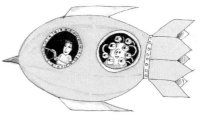

written and illustrated by

Ed Boxall

troika

Me and My Alien Friend...

...ARE THE VERY BEST OF THE BESTEST...

...HAVE SOME DIFFICULT AND CONFUSING...

...HAVE FOUR AND FOURTEEN LEGGED...

...HAVE SOME BITTY BOBBY BITTY...

...AND SOME FARAWAY AND MAGIC...

...BUT OUR FAMILIES ARE THE OLDEST...

...FRIENDS!

THE VERY BEST OF THE BESTEST FRIENDS

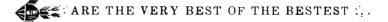

You're Here!!

for a friend you haven't seen for a while

You're a perfect day
In a human shape
I'm glad we're back
In the same place

Because I talk to you
About everything
I usually whisper
But with you I sing!

Super Hero at My Door

I woke up and knew today
would be down in the grot and grey
down in the grot and grey
just like yesterday

the moaning morning mist
easily convinced
the surly sun to sulk behind
the dirty curtain sky.

So I went back to bed
and pulled the duvet
over my head.

THE END.

 Until . . .

  . . . at 9:59 Mum said

'Jack's coming round at 10
you better be up by then.'
When I heard your friendly rat-a-tat
I jumped up in a FLASH.

Like a super hero at the door
you made me teleport
to before life's colours changed
from rainbow shades to grey.

Then you pulled the sun from out behind
the dirty curtain sky
and said 'Let's play with this!'
and gave it a massive kick.

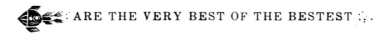

It blazed past Mum and made her SCREAM
and broke some worries I didn't need
then with cards and games and your bright smile
you saved my world before lunch time.

With the super power of being you
and knowing me the way you do
you made me forget to be sad
you are a super hero, Jack.

How Did We End Up Talking About..?

Walking along,
Banging big sticks on the gravelly ground,
with a lazy
1......2.....
crunching sound...

How did we end up talking about...bleach
for 15 minutes at least?

What is that stuff?
And plasticine?
And lentils?
Are there bleach reservoirs, plasticine mines and
lentil trees?
Or are they all made in factories?

Walking along,
Banging big sticks on the earthy ground,
with a lazy
1......2.....
thudding sound...

How did we end up talking about rhubarb
for 15 minutes at least?

Rhubarb is a good word, we agreed.

So we shared our other favourite words:
Mine were lemon, dark, and mandolin
Yours were binturong, and pangolin.

Walking along,
Banging big sticks on the hard ground,
with a lazy
1......2.....
whacking sound...

How did we end up talking about bumblebees
for 15 minutes at least?

...we wondered whether bumblebees know they
    are bumblebees
(we thought probably not)
but that they probably knew they were
    something different
to a spider, football or a rock.

Or you, or me.

**Walking along,
Banging big sticks on the familiar ground,
with a lazy
1......2......
coming home sound...**

I love how we talk
about everything and nothing
two best friends walking through
    the universe
the word rhubarb
shining in my mind
like a bright new planet.

See you later
Smelly Alligator!

Just Like Us

My mum and dad have an allotment.
They've been there a lot this Summer.
Digging, planting, mowing
and talking about
digging planting mowing
while they stand staring
at the ground
with folded arms.

While they're doing that
I can go wherever I want
as long as I stay on the allotments.
So soon as we get there
I run off and see if Noah is around.

It's good if he is.
We go off and jump the ditch
to Soren's garden.
We get him,
and head down
to No one's Land.

No one's Land
is the wild bit at the bottom of the allotments
that no one owns and no one goes to except us.

You gotta have a big stick
to bash away brambles,
in No one's Land.

You gotta have long trousers
or you get stung by nettles,
in No one's Land.

You gotta have plenty of sweets
in case you get lost,
in No one's Land.

We've never found the back of No one's Land
but we have found a rusty bicycle wheel,
an old TV (with all the weird valves
    like spaceships and robots)
and a loads of old glass bottles that look
like they were once filled with poison.

And today we found
a door in a wall of ivy
that fell off when I opened it.

Behind it was utterly dark
until our sundazzled eyes adjusted,
and saw cobwebs hiding in the corners,
and ivy bursting through the windows
of a long abandoned garden shed.

The dull light slowly found,
a tidy line of old bottles arranged against the wall,
faded sweet wrappers scattered on the floor,
3 big, well chosen sticks leaning up,
3 chairs covered in years of dust,
3 names carved in the wall:
James, Ralph, George.

Noah said

'Just like us'

We could never find that shed again.

Ultimate Heroes

We were ultimate heroes
of playtime games,
Batman versus Superman
Flash verses Dr Strange.

When did we change?

Spinning. Racing.
Red in face,
Lasers in our fingers
On a death chase through space.

How did we change?

Now we're back at our old school,
For our little brothers' school play
Ultimate heroes...

...with nothing much to say.

Why did we change?

Watching the ghosts,
of who we were then,
In the playground on the way home.
Heroes?
Friends?
Friends.

After The Party

My friends have gone home now.
I'm in bed.
I hear the grown ups talking and laughing downstairs.
Tonight we played sardines, top trumps, stick fights, rope swing,
and pile up on the trampoline.
We've eaten pizza, crisps, garlic bread, cheese puffs,
chocolate raisins and absolutely no cucumber sticks.
Now the grown ups are singing really loudly.
I like hearing them.
Behind their voices I hear cars going by in the street,
A pigeon cooing.
The world humming and the trees growing.
Mum comes in quietly. She thinks I'm asleep.
She says 'I love you'
The grown ups' voices are rippling and splashing.
Their laughter is a shoal of silver fish that are swimming
all around my body and glistening in the underwater sunlight.
I didn't know I could swim...I didn't know my toy rabbit
could swim...
The friendly laughing fish make this a safe place.
We dive way down sparkly pebbly underwater hills.
I think I'm asleep now.

Campfire Caterpillars

We are in our sleeping bags by the campfire
out later than we've ever been up outside before.
Campfire Caterpillars. Best friends.

The laughing from all the fires on the campsite
makes a warm ring of safety around us
to let the wolves and wandering scarecrows
know to stay away.

We have been talking for hours.
But now we are watching smoke drift silently up and
over the trees.

There are no walls around us
no floor underneath us
and no roof between us and the universes
we see up there
billions of light years away.

Let's never go back.
Let's live like this in the woods
with the wolves and wandering scarecrows.
Campfire Caterpillars. Best Friends.

Mixed Up Mean Team

Mixed Up Mean Team is a game
that is quite like Funny Nose
but not a bit like Basic Mean Team.
Mixed up Mean Team
is much more basic.

It's got no rules but
my brother and me
are the only ones
who know them all off by heart.

It takes years to learn them
but we only invented it this morning.

All the rules are strictly secret.
We will never tell you them.
NEVER NEVER NEVER.
First Rule: only an even number of people
  can play.

Second Rule: don't be mean.
Third Rule: it's not a team game
but we'll make a great team, us three.

You won't understand
it if you miss the beginning,
but join in any time
it never really began.

It has no end but, sorry, it's just finished.
Come back tomorrow.
Where are you going??
Mixed Up Mean team
is just about to start!

Let's play Mixed Up Mean Team!!

the silence as we draw

the silence as we draw
is a huge calm lake
hidden in the forest
our secret place

bright fish appear
in the darkest deep
they break the surface
every time we speak

they leap and dance
and splash with laughter
leaving ripples of thought
a long time after

the silence as we draw
is a deep calm lake
far in the forest
our secret place

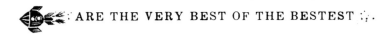

Fun Run

I can't run fast and I get out of breath,
When I try to keep up with Jemma and Beth,
I don't understand why they always want to win,
Seems they get to the end before I even begin.

So I thought a 'School Fun Run' an awful idea,
I couldn't escape a terrible fear,
I dreaded the thought that I'd come last,
And all of the school would cruelly laugh.

Well today was The Run and I changed my mind,
I learnt to run can be fun when you're left behind,
'Cos I got to know Jack at the back like me,
He said 'just enjoy moving don't think about speed.'

I'd never spoken to him before but he's really alright,
In fact we're going roller-skating later tonight,
Well when we turned a corner, here's the surprise,
Jem and Beth were waiting for us to arrive.

We all ran together to the finish line,
We all jumped across at just the right time,
We all ran together to the finish line,
We all jumped across at just the right time.

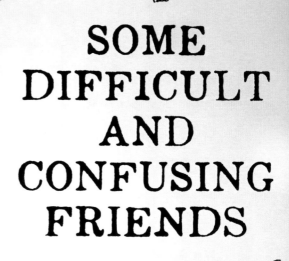

SOME
DIFFICULT
AND
CONFUSING
FRIENDS

Jamie

There was a bad smell in assembly today,
a ripple of whispers and laughs.

Afterwards in class,
Jamie got blamed.

I don't know why.
Perhaps because he wears old clothes
and is shy.
Very shy.

He never said a word
as everyone teased him.

Everyone.

I joined in at first.

But it went on all day.

And Jamie looked like he'd forgotten how to smile
and would never laugh again.

I've never seen anyone as sad and hurt as Jamie today.

The Friendship Game

Friendship is a game with difficult rules,
That no one properly teaches to you.

So let's go back to school, the subject is friendship today,
We're doing it in an ordered, straightforward, bullet-pointed way.

Before we begin there's something I must explain,
There's a complicated language to this complicated game.

There's odd words and analogies, and at the end of the day,
Let's face it: a mountain of clichés.

Lesson 1: Tact

We must learn, the mystic power known as 'tact',
No talking at the back! This is hard to understand:

So, 'honesty is the best policy', apart from when it's not, and
It's really a bad policy really quite a lot.

Say you don't want to play, on Saturday with Dave,
It could hurt his feelings if you come out and say that straight.

This is one of those times, it hurts to tell the truth,
Tell him you've got to dig a hole, or some other good excuse.

Lesson 2: Play it Cool

This means be nice but not *too* nice,
Nobody has ever discovered how to get this balance right.

Let's say instead you *want* to play, on Saturday with Dave,
Don't follow him round all Friday or you might scare him away.

Don't fill his house with flowers or 'Please Play with Me' balloons,
And don't break all his pencils if he won't play with you.

Lesson 3: Conversational Turn-taking

Don't talk about yourself too much,
  but don't keep things bottled up,
Somehow you've got to know when your friends have had enough.

To give friends time to choose their words,
  is nearly always good,
But sense when a silence is getting...

awkward.

Sorry class. I have to stop.
I've just realised,
I've got as much to learn as you lot.

'Tact?' 'conversational turn taking??' 'play it cool???'
I don't get this language.
I can't teach the rules.

The best friends that I've got,
are the ones who really don't mind,
If I know the rules or not.

I can't teach this subject.

Just do your best.

Lesson over.

It's All So Easy For You

(this poem can be shouted angrily)

Your hand goes up faster than mine
So the teacher picks you every time

It's All so Easy For You
It's All so Easy For You

When there's a smell you're never blamed,
You're good at every single game

It's All so Easy For You
It's All so Easy For You

They always choose you to show visitors round,
You're never lost and lonely in the playground

It's All so Easy For You
It's All so Easy For You

The teacher tells you 'aren't you bright!'
And shares her jokes and brightest smiles.

It's All so Easy For You
It's All so Easy For You

Is there a nice heart-warming end?
Do we end up best of friends?

Not today.

Me, You, and Sue.

We were two,
me and you.

Best friends.

I even told you
my absolutely
secret secret.

But along came Sue
to our school
and you and Sue
were the brand new two.

And I was one alone.

Like a popped balloon
after a party
when everyone's gone home.

And you and Sue
were too
fake nice to me
like it was a job you had to do,

but didn't really want to.

And I knew,
we would never
again be two

because you
told Sue
my absolutely secret secret.

I Don't Know Why You Lie

Go away!
Leave us alone!
You talk too much
and your jokes are bad.

Go away!
Leave us alone!
You tell lies
and always brag.

You talk in exclamation marks!!
About your imaginary racing car!!

And how your dad is a big pop star!!!
And about how very very rich you are!!!

I don't know why you are always lying
I don't know why you were quietly crying
walking home alone looking very small
like you didn't want to be seen at all.

I don't know why
you lie
it makes it hard
to be
your friend.

-but whatever
anyone else says-

I'll try

Awkward Silence

There was an awkward silence because
I hadn't seen Beth for ages.

The words 'Awkward Silence'
jumped out of my mouth,without me asking.

We both laughed and the awkward silence was gone.

So, the next time there was an awkward silence,
with my mum and my nan
and Jane and Brad having tea

I said 'Awkward Silence,'

and waited for people to laugh.

But everyone just stared down
at their lasagne silently

and the silence got longer and longer and I went red,

and ran up stairs.

I don't understand.

But my friends understand me.
I can't wait to tell them this story

Telling them will make
it all okay,
And this awful embarrassed
feeling will go away.

I Will Live In A Tree house
And Look After The Animals

You were going to walk to school with me.
You agreed.
You said you'd call for me at 8:15.

I waited a long time.
You never came.

I got to school late.

You were there already,
sitting on a table laughing with everyone.

You said 'oh sorry I forgot' as if it didn't
matter at all.

So I am going to climb a jungle tree,
build a tree house,
And look after the animals.

I will be fine.
I will be free:
The parrots, monkeys, bears and me.

You'll never find me there.
In the great huge swaying canopy,
among the creaking branches,
and rustling leaves,
where the wolves,
prowl below
protecting me from enemies.

SOME FOUR AND FOURTEEN LEGGED FRIENDS

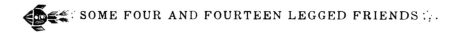

Dixie

When I was 4
Dixie came to stay,
She was just a puppy then,
I wanted her to be my best friend.
But I chased her,
I squeezed her,
I loved her
So much
I nearly cuddled off her head.
That's what Mum said.
I don't think I would have cuddled off her head,
But she really didn't want to be my friend.
So the tears rose up in my throat and poured out,
'Why doesn't she love me?' I'd shout.

Now I am 10
I don't chase her
I don't squeeze her
I don't tease her
I love her
Much more gently.

So when I was too poorly to read
And even watching TV gave me a headache
She curled up on the sofa with me.
Best friends at last.

Daisy

Daisy is my family's cat,
But she is my best friend,
She's the only one allowed inside
My box and blanket den.

I've filled it up with duvets
And all our favourite foods,
I climb inside and very soon,
She follows me in for a snooze.

I always read her a book,
Before she goes to sleep,
She likes stories of Koala Bears,
They give her cosy dreams.

She curls up on my shoulder,
That's her favourite place,
She squeaks a quick meow,
When it's time to turn the page.

When we sleep the den is a ship,
And we are stowaways,
And the movement of her breathing,
Is the sighing of the waves.

We sail above the world,
On seas of big grey clouds,
Over Europe, over Africa,
Over mountains, forests, and towns.

Daisy is my family's cat,
But she is my best friend,
She's the only one allowed inside
My box and blanket den.

Jimmy The Woodlouse

Jimmy came in,
in a big bag of potatoes from the garden.

I liked him right away.

Quick on his feet
and sensitive under his hard outer shell.
We had a lot in common.

He was friendly
and curious
like a puppy in a park
as he ran across the back of my hand.

I made him a home in a plastic takeaway container.
I gave him some moss,
a bottle top of water
and put holes in the top of his
takeaway-container-bungalow.

I liked Jimmy
I really did.
I liked him a lot.

But life is busy...

...and by the time
I'd finished my dinner
and watched TV
I'd forgotten him completely.

Oops.

3 weeks later
I found that takeaway container
on the floor by the dirty outdoor shoes.
Uh oh.
I prepared myself for the worst
and opened up the lid.

But there he was.
Alive and well
and shaking all his 14 legs angrily
like he was challenging me to a boxing match.

I thought
maybe I'm not ready
for the responsibility
of being a good woodlouse guardian
and so set him free
under the tree.

When I let him go
he waved his 14 legs at me,
In a gesture that really didn't look friendly.

Sorry Jimmy.

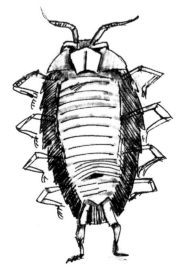

My Walk to School Friends

Swishing tails, silent paws,
Staring through windows, dozing on walls,
I say hello to my walk-to-school friends:
Butcher, Beowolf, Belinda and Ben.

Butcher. Edwin Road. Number 22.
Big black cat. Bad attitude.
He glares with angry disapproving eyes,
And greets a stroke with a scratch and bite.

Swishing tails, silent paws,
Staring through windows, dozing on walls,
I say hello to my walk-to-school friends:
Butcher, Beowolf, Belinda and Ben

Beowolf. Peel Street. Number 38.
Like a big grey cloud with a squirrel tail,
When I stroke his tummy he thunderously purrs,
But he's a tiny skinny cat under all that fur.

Swishing tails, silent paws,
Staring through windows, dozing on walls,
I say hello to my walk-to-school friends:
Butcher, Beowolf, Belinda and Ben

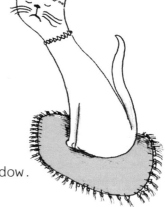

Belinda. Queen Street. Number 33,
Really believes that she's royalty,
On satin pillows on her high throne,
Stares down her nose from the attic window.

Swishing tails, silent paws,
Staring through windows, dozing on walls,
I say hello to my walk-to-school friends:
Butcher, Beowolf, Belinda and Ben

Ben. Duke Street. Number 21.
Old pirate cat whose travels are done.
He tells gory stories to the kittens at night,
About how his tail got bent and he lost his left eye.

Swishing tails, silent paws,
Staring through windows, dozing on walls,
I say bye to my walk-to-school friends:
Butcher, Beowolf, Belinda and Ben

SOME BITTY BOBBY
BITTY FRIENDS

A Thing on a Springy String

I am friends with a thing,
A thing on a springy string,
I don't know what it is, but I like it.
My thing on a string.

It sleeps under my pillow,
I hold it there all night,
As it glows just a little,
with a warm comforting light.

When I hold it tight,
The rustling against my ear,
And the scary thoughts as I try to sleep,
Are something I can bear.

When the nightmares gallop,
On the ground of thundering screams,
I throw my thing at them,
And they smash to smithereens.

And my thing on a springy string,
Pings right back to me,
And I have good dreams of dolphins leaping,
the sparkly sunny sea.

I am friends with a thing,
A thing on a springy string,
I don't know what it is, but I like it.
My thing on a string.

Scabadabba

I've grown to like my scab.
I call her Scabadabba.
For short I call her Scab.

She's my friend.
We've done a lot together,
since I first got scratched

on the first day of the holiday,
when I fell out of the tree
and the ground attacked.

Since then we've scrambled
    under brambles,
Found rat and rabbit skulls,
with Rose and Jack.

We found an old bike wheel,
and an ancient television,
behind the garden backs.

Where the days felt like forever,
with the woodlice and the birds,
it was our secret land.

She's stayed with me all Summer,
but it's time to pick her off,
but I don't feel sad.

I'm keeping her forever,
in a little matchbox
perfect size for Scab.

I'm taking her to school,
to remind me of the Summer,
because tomorrow we go back.

40

Sometimes

Sometimes my best and only friend is a rubber band.

Like when Miss Pettit is going on and on
and I feel like I have to run out the room
and stretch and growl and shake my arms.
If I could do that I'd be fine but you can't
run out the room and stretch and growl and
shake your arms.

You just can't.

So I play with my rubber band instead.
I concentrate on it and nothing else.
I wind it round and round my finger
so tight it hurts.

But that's better than
running out the room and stretching and growling and
shaking my arms or shouting at Miss Pettit
and getting excluded again.

Umbrella

It rained on the way
to school this morning.

When I left the sun was shining,
so I didn't bring my coat.

It came down heavy and fast.

Icy cold pounding on my head,
soaking through my blazer,
dripping down my neck,
leaving dark cold soggy
patches on my legs.

It rained on the way
to school this morning
and it was the best thing ever.

I was walking along,
my head down,
moving as quick as I could,
when the rain stopped falling on me.

I could hear it,
I could see it,
but I couldn't feel it on my head.

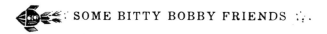

I looked up.
I was under an umbrella.
And Sophie was holding it.

She said 'you look wet.'

'Thank you' I said and felt
myself go very very red.
And that was all I said,
because I forgot how to speak.

She said 'bye' when we got to school,
and folded up her umbrella.
I tried to reply but could
only manage a smile.

She looked straight at me,
and smiled back.
My stomach felt like
when we're in the car
and we go down a hill really fast.

I floated a centimetre
or two above the ground.

And I'm still floating now.

Where Everything Is My Friend

Why don't you sit down here?
It's a great place to sit and draw.
Nature made this area flatter and tidier than the rest of
the forest.
I found it. It was made just for me, just for this
holiday.
Animal paths led me here to a flat soft grassy seat,
surrounded by mossy rocks.
There are little fur trees next to me. The tops are level
with my eyes like I'm a giant.
Tiny ones are growing at my feet.

It's a garden in a wilderness.

My tooth is loose, I fiddle with it and look up at the
straight trees that are a hundred times taller than me.

Ants like it here.

There are mossy patches at my feet that are jungle
islands. There are whole other planets of jungle islands
somewhere in space. Anything you could think of is
somewhere out there.

Leaves shake gently as a bee buzzes.

Birds sing but don't come too close.
A woodpecker lives up there—
I saw him go into a round tree hole.
He hasn't come out yet.
Breeze moves the high branches.

My home is a thousand miles away.

This is my secret place, where I am friends with
everything and everything is my friend.

SOME FARAWAY AND
MAGIC FRIENDS

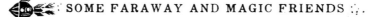

Me and My Alien Friend

Me and my alien friend,
Sit on the moon and eat ice cream.

It's quiet up here.

**We swing our legs we stretch out toes
And look down on the world below**

Me and my alien friend,
Talk around the universes
In the spaceships of conversation
Never knowing where we'll end up.

**We swing our legs we stretch out toes
And look down on the world below**

Me and my alien friend, don't mind
. . . .
. . . .
long pauses

**We swing our legs we stretch out toes
And look down on the world below**

Me and my alien friend,
Throw stones at passing satellites.
But we never hit.
Our stones float
up up up
and float on forever
through distant galaxies.

**We swing our legs we stretch out toes
And look down on the world below**

I see my toenails need a cut
His toenails *really* need a cut

But he has 38 toes so it's a job he puts off doing,
However much his mum asks.

Just like me and tidying my room
Or doing my homework.

We swing our legs we stretch out toes
And look down on the world below

We look past our 48 toes,
And see the world is shining like treasure,
In a perfectly clear pool—
As beautiful and fragile
As friendship.

It's time to go home.
If our mums call three times
We know we've got to go
Or there's trouble.

We swing our legs we stretch out toes
And look down on the world below

We swing our legs we stretch out toes
And look down on the world below

Me and my Human Friend

My Human Friend is a good friend,
but he never invites me to his world.

We've never had a sleepover.

He has told me there are millions
    just like him:

2 legs.
10 toes
2 arms
8 fingers
2 thumbs

Weird.

I don't know how they get anything done.

I'd like to go there one day.
'Pizza and a film marathon' sounds
    a lot of fun.

But, he's a good friend
and he wants to keep me safe.
And he says his world is
often a dangerous and cruel place
and he couldn't trust them
to be kind
to someone with 7 legs
38 toes and 6 eyes.

Weird.

THE TWILIGHT DRAGON

After school when everyone was tired,
When Dad was on his laptop
And Mum was on the phone,

I'd climb the tree,
And leave the garden far beneath,
The Twilight Dragon was at the top,
Waiting for me.

His feathers would flutter,
With every sunset colour,
Pink magenta red yellow and gold,

I'd climb up
His heart beating under my feet,
And find a strong feather to hold.
Very tightly.

Me and the only dragon
In the universe,
Would fly silently

Over the factories
The chimneys
The cities
To the wide open sea

Faraway from the noise and chatter of my day
Over the horizon,
To his home behind the sky

We'd wander for hours,
Talking as we explored,
His deep blue mountain lakes,
His rivers and empty moors.

In the distance,
I'd hear Dad say dinner's ready.
Across time I hear him now.

The Twilight Dragon
Is still alive as on those evenings,
When I'm alone and very silent,
I still find him.

He's the only dragon
In the universe,
He's alone, like me.

Anyone could see him
If they looked up
But they never look up
They never see.

Winter Wanderer

I've seen you around town,
Wandering alone
No one else seems to have noticed you
So far from your land of snow.

You're always, always walking,
Do you never go home?
Always, always walking
Have you even got a home?

When I pass you in the street,
You never meet my eye
You look so tired and sad
Are there worries on your mind?

I wonder do you miss
The whisper of the pines
As you hunted through the night
In your far fields of ice.

To see you sends my dreams
Drifting with the snowflakes
I'd love to know you better
Surely we could make space.

For a homesick polar bear,
To come over and stay,
Even if it's not forever
At least for Christmas day.

FAMILY ARE THE OLDEST FRIENDS

Rainbow Layered cake

It's icy and cold outside in the street.
Bitter rain. Stinging Sleet.
Two silver forks, a giant white plate.
I'm with Dad, in the cafe, sharing rainbow layered cake,

I was scared of the dentist, but it was alright.
Relief makes each colour taste especially bright.
They'll be starting maths, just about now,
But we're sipping hot choc, with marshmallows in town.

But the thing that's mostly making me smile,
Is seeing Dad with no worries or tears in his eyes.
This dad that I haven't seen for a while,
has found the sunshine, and brought it inside.

So could I have just one more treat?
Could this moment last forever please?

Scootering in the Hospital

I am fed up of this waiting room.
Nobody smiles.
And I can't do anything without
Getting in trouble.

No sliding on the shiny corridor floors.
No playing on my phone.
No talking silly.
No fighting with my brother.

Mum's no fun because Grandad's sick.

She just said 'Grow up. Sit still.'

I CANNOT SIT STILL ANYMORE
I CANNOT GROW UP.

Not today. Why should I?

So I get on my scooter.

Out the door,
Foot slapping the floor,
Building up speed,
Can't catch me,
Clatter down stairs,
Jump wheel chairs,
I'm not scared,
I just don't care
Building up speed,
You can't catch me,
Knock doctors down,
Spin nurses round

Trolleys crash.
Medicine smash
Building up speed,
You can't catch me,

Winning the race
Winning the race

Against...?
Against...?

Against Sad Feeling...
Sad Feeling in my chest,
In my throat.
And pouring out my eyes.

It's won. It caught me.
I didn't stand a chance.

Mum looks at me and holds my hand tight,
She smiles and says
'I need you to look after me'

We walk together out of the waiting room.
We walk into Grandad's calm white room.

I hold Mum's hand tight.

Didn't Mean To

We didn't mean to
empty out all our toys.
We didn't mean to
make all that noise.

We didn't mean to,
play football inside.

OK. We did.

We did mean to do those things,
    you're right.
But we didn't mean to smash the light.

Like a forest fire it happened so fast.
And yes,
of course,
we'll sweep up the glass.

So now
we're sweeping up
silently
we're putting our toys away
politely.

I wonder what our punishment will be...

...Oh NO.
Oh no no no,

A little laugh has appeared inside of me.
Don't look at me.
You'll make it grow,

Oh no.
Oh no no no

We'll make it a thousand times worse
I'm trying to frown
but I just want to smirk.

Hate this feeling.
Love this feeling.

Like a firework this laugh will EXPLODE.
There's nothing I can do about it now

here goes...

hee hee hur hur ha ha ha heeeeeee Hee eee
hurr hur HA (snort)
HA HEEEEE

I can see our punishment getting bigger
and bigger in Dad's angry eyes..
A gargantuan punishment to fill the skies

HAA HA HA heee HEE HA HA HA HA HA HA
 (snorty gurgle)
HA HA HA HA HA HA
HA...................

No Screen time for a week.
That's fair.
Was it worth it?
Yeah.

My 10ᵗʰ Birthday

Last year,
on my 9ᵗʰ birthday,
Everyone piled into my room
like a herd of rhinos
on a sugar high.

Every toy in every drawer
ended up on the floor.

And weeks later I found something rotten
and wet in my dressing up box
that I think might have once been a piece of
birthday cake.

I didn't mind at all.

After my 10ᵗʰ birthday party,
which, by the way
was today.
Everyone did pretty much the same.

But I suddenly knew when
Alfie and Jack and James
were in my room
everything had changed.

I didn't want them in my space.

When my guitar got broke
and James looked at my private drawings
I felt a crying choke in my throat.
And I needed them to go.
And leave me alone.
Right away. Out my room. Right now.

I couldn't speak. I couldn't tell them.

Mum knew.
She put on a film downstairs.
And got them all to watch it
without letting on why they had to leave my room.

Now my room is empty.
Just me.

Any minute now I'm going downstairs
to watch the film.

Any minute now.

Boulders

You will never be too old
To ride upon my shoulders
Even when you're six foot tall
And heavier than boulders

About the Author:

Ed Boxall is a childrens' poet, illustrator, musician, educator and performer.
He has written and illustrated many book s, such as *Mr Trim* and *Miss
Jumble* for Walker Books and *High In The Old Oak Tree* for his own Pearbox
Press. Ed performs his poems with a mix of spoken word, projections at
schools, art centres and festivals. He lives in Hastings, a small town
on the south coast of England.

www.edboxall.com